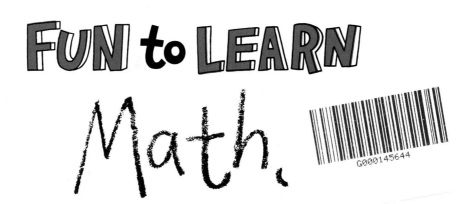

FUN to LEARN
Math.

Peter Patilla
Illustrated by Andy Cooke

Educational Advisory Panel

Bernard Ashley – Head teacher and author

Diana Bentley – Language adviser

Peter Patilla – Lecturer and author

Susie Sainsbury – Nursery teacher

WALKER BOOKS
AND SUBSIDIARIES
LONDON · BOSTON · SYDNEY · AUCKLAND

Notes to Parents

Mathematics is not a difficult subject: in this series of books, the basic mathematical concepts are introduced through activities that are tremendous fun to do and to share. To children, each page is a game; for parents there is the reassuring knowledge that the activities are worthwhile and that they reinforce the children's work at school.

In order to help your children:
* talk through the activities and listen well to their responses
* encourage them to talk about the pictures as much as the mathematics involved
* talk about different approaches to each question, rather than imposing one method of working
* praise them frequently
* don't do too much in one session, but let children return to the pages they enjoy most

Notes on the educational purpose of each topic are listed below, with a reference in brackets to the specific subject area covered.

1 How many?
(Number)
Practice in adding. Several sets are to be added together.
Which creatures are there most of?
Which creatures are there fewest of?
How many creatures don't have arms?

2 Counting and pairing
(Number)
This is simple problem solving, followed by counting.
How many 4-legged animals?
How many 2-legged animals?
How many legs altogether?

3 Taking away
(Number)
Taking away from sets.
Play snatcher games – have a set of items and let children play at being a 1-snatcher, 2-snatcher etc.
Look at a set of items and secretly take away a number of them and let children guess which "snatcher" has been.

4 Where on the line?
(Number)
Counting and the position of numbers.
Use words like: next to, after, between, before, first, last.
What is the odd sock?
Which do you wear?

5 Numbers in patterns
(Number)
Counting and showing that numbers can be arranged in different patterns.
There are three patterns shown for nine, eight and six. Give children a number of small objects to arrange in different patterns. Encourage them to try to describe each pattern made.

6 Matching patterns
(Number)
Recognizing patterns. Encourage children to describe the patterns.
How many heads?
How many tails?
Which snakes have spots on their yellow stripes?
Which snakes have patterns with only one spot?

7 Finishing patterns
(Algebra)
Early ideas of algebra. Children have to try to find the missing parts by looking at the pattern. Encourage children to make repetitive patterns with crayons and to paint zigzag patterns. They could also try printing patterns with potatoes.

8 Number game
This game involves children in counting forwards and backwards. Encourage them to make their own rules for landing on the red and blue spots.

9 Night and day
(Measures)
These pictures are to encourage children to discuss what happens over the passage of time.
Who works during the day?
Which animals come out at night?
How does the night sky differ from the day sky?
What do you do in the daytime?

10 Bigger and smaller
(Measures)
Early ideas of measurement. Children should be encouraged to use language of comparison wherever appropriate, for example: longer, shorter, thinner, wider, thicker, heavier, lighter, etc.

11 Find the shape
(Shape and space)
This activity is to allow children to recognize and talk about solid shapes. The names of the shapes are: cube, cuboid, sphere, cylinder.
It is not necessary for children to know the names at this stage. Sorting the food store cupboard will encourage recognition of different shapes.

12 Finding more shapes
(Shape and space)
Recognizing and talking about flat shapes. The names of the shapes are: square, rectangle, circle and diamond. It is not necessary for children to know the names at this stage. Encourage them to look for these shapes in the home environment.

13 Patterns and shapes
(Shape and space)
This activity is concerned with recognizing pattern in shape. Slices of fruit and vegetables offer a rich variety of shape and pattern. Cut slices from fruit and vegetables at home for children to recognize.

14 Simple graphs
(Handling data)
Experience of handling data. This is an important skill and children should be encouraged to look at a wide variety of charts, timetables, lists, diagrams, etc. where information is shown. Who does not have a cat? Which two children have a dog? Which pet does Ian have?

1 How many?

How many of each of these can you find?

2 Counting and pairing

Match up the pairs of animals.
Which is the odd one out?

How many ears can you find?
And how many tails?

3 Taking away

Here is a red snatcher. When it sees sets
of red things it snatches two of them.
Look for the red sets. How many will each
set have left after it has been?

Here is a blue snatcher. When it sees sets of blue things it snatches three of them.
Look for the blue sets. How many will each set have left after it has been?

4 Where on the line?

How many socks are there?
How many spotty clothes are there?
How many green clothes are there?

What is between the sheet and the vests?
What is next to the socks?

5 Numbers in patterns

Can you match these elephants into sets of three?
Here's a clue: count the spots to find the sets.

Which elephant is the odd one out?

6 Matching patterns

Match the right heads to
their tails.
Here's a clue: count
the spots on the blue
stripes and the
yellow stripes.

Which head has no tail?

7 Finishing patterns

Find the missing buttons.
Which colour is right for the pattern on each coat?

One carriage is missing on each train.
What does the missing carriage look like?

8 Number game

Start

No
Fishing

Use a die and counters.
Good things happen on red spots:
move forward one spot.
Nasty things happen on blue spots:
move back one spot.
Play the game.

Make your own good rule
for red spots.
Make your own nasty rule
for blue spots.
Now play the game
by these rules.

9 Night and day

What differences can you find between
these two times of day?

What happens at night?
What happens in the daytime?

10 Bigger and smaller

Which are the largest shoes?

Which shoes have the highest heels?

Which shoes have the longest laces?

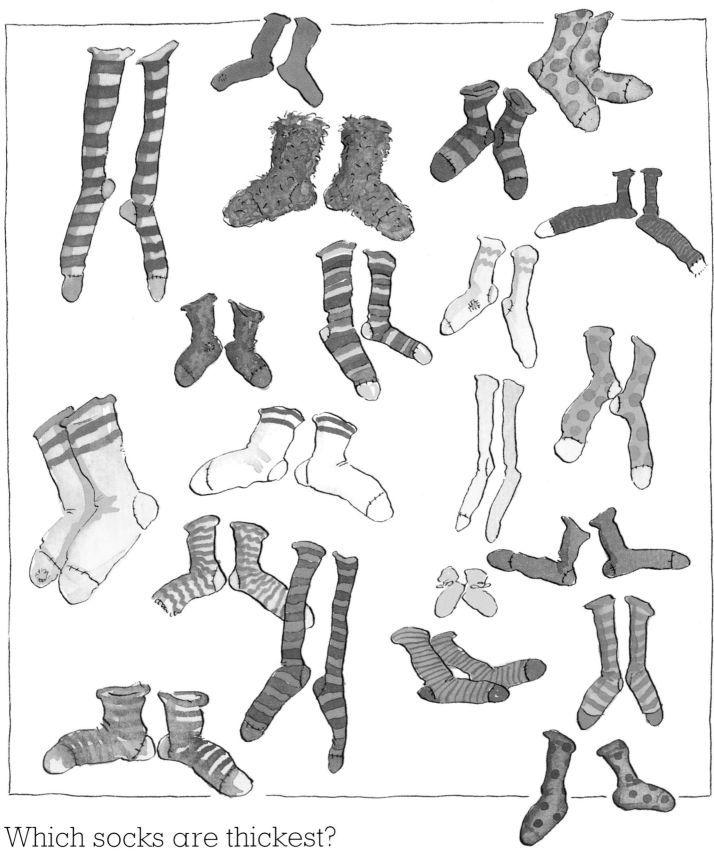

Which socks are thickest?

Which socks are smallest?

Which socks have the most colours?

11 Find the shape

Can you find shapes like these?

12 Finding more shapes

Can you find shapes like these?

13 Patterns and shapes

Look at these patterns.
What do they come from?

Match up the slices with the whole fruits
and vegetables.

14 Simple graphs

This graph shows some children's pets.

Lee   Michelle David   Claire   Jayne   Ian

Which pets do you think belong to each child?
The graph will help you.

Answers

1 How many?
There are 6 green monsters; 4 red; 9 yellow; 7 blue.

2 Counting and pairing
The zebra is the odd one out.

3 Taking away
The red snatcher will leave 8 balls, 1 car, 4 inflatable toys, 2 robots.

The blue snatcher will leave 6 cubes, 5 boats, 3 aeroplanes.

4 Where on the line?
There are 5 socks, 6 spotty clothes, 6 green clothes.

There are towels between the sheets and the vests.

There are shorts and handkerchiefs next to the socks.

5 Numbers in patterns?
The odd one out is the elephant with 7 spots.

6 Matching patterns?
The snake with one spot on the purple stripe and no spots on the yellow stripe has no tail.

7 Finishing patterns
The yellow button goes on the blue coat; the red button on the pink coat; the blue button on the woman's purple coat; the purple button on the guard's coat; the green button on the man's grey coat; the brown button on the brown coat.

From top to bottom the missing carriages are: carriage with light blue roof; red carriage; brown truck; blue carriage; carriage with three windows.

10 Bigger and smaller
The largest shoes are the brown clown's shoes; the highest shoes are the red shoes with blue bows; the longest laces are on the football boots.

The blue woolly socks are the thickest; the yellow socks are the smallest; the multicoloured striped socks have the most colours.

13 Patterns and shapes
The fruits and vegetables on the left hand page are arranged as follows:

carrot; orange
peach; cucumber
apple; tomato

First published 1990 by Walker Books Ltd
87 Vauxhall Walk, London SE11 5HJ

This edition published 2003

10 9 8 7 6 5 4 3 2 1

Text © 1990 Peter Patilla
Illustrations © 1990 Andy Cooke

The right of Peter Patilla and Andy Cooke to be identified as author and illustrator respectively of this work has been asserted by them in accordance with the Copyright, Designs and Patents Act 1988

This book has been typeset in Rockwell Light Educational

Printed in China

British Library Cataloguing in Publication Data:
a catalogue record for this book is available from the British Library

ISBN 1-84428-808-0

www.walkerbooks.co.uk